This book is
your passport
into time.

Can you survive
in the
Age of Knights?
Turn the page
to find out.

Bantam Books in the Time Machine Series

TIME MACHINE 1

Secret
of the Knights

by Jim Gasperini
illustrated by Richard Hescox

A Byron Preiss Book

BANTAM BOOKS
TORONTO · NEW YORK · LONDON · SYDNEY

RL 4, IL age 10 and up

SECRET OF THE KNIGHTS
A Bantam Book/February 1984

Special thanks to Judy Gitenstein, Ann Weil, Ron Buehl, Anne
Greenberg, Nancy Pines, David Harris, and Lucy Salvino.

Book design by Alex Jay.
Cover painting by Richard Hescox.
Cover design by Alex Jay.
Mechanicals by Susan Leung and Studio J.
Typesetting by Graphic/Data Services

"Time Machine" is a trademark of Byron
Preiss Visual Publications, Inc.

ISBN 0-553-23601-6

Published simultaneously in the United States and Canada

PRINTED IN THE UNITED STATES OF AMERICA

0 9 8 7 6 5 4 3 2 1

ATTENTION TIME TRAVELER!

This book is your time machine. Do not read it through from beginning to end. In a moment you will receive a mission, a special task that will take you to another time period. As you face the dangers of history, the Time Machine often will give you options of where to go or what to do.

This book also contains a Data Bank to tell you about the age you are going to visit. You can use this Data Bank to travel more safely through time. Or you can take your chances without reading it. It is up to you to decide.

In the back of this book is a Data File. It contains hints to help you if you are not sure what choice to make. The following symbol appears next to any choices for which there is a hint in the Data File.

To complete your mission as quickly as possible, you may wish to use the Data Bank and the Data File together.

There is one correct end to this Time Machine mission. You must reach it or risk being stranded in time!

THE FOUR RULES OF TIME TRAVEL

As you begin your mission, you must observe the following rules. Time Travelers who do not follow these rules risk being stranded in time.

1. You must not kill any person or animal.

2. You must not try to change history. Do not leave anything from the future in the past.

3. You must not take anybody when you jump in time. Avoid disappearing in a way that scares people or makes them suspicious.

4. You must follow instructions given to you by the Time Machine. You must choose from the options given to you by the Time Machine.

YOUR MISSION

You mission is to become a knight, and then find out how the most famous order, or group, of English knights got its name.

For six hundred years, the highest honor in England has been to be made a knight of the Order of the Garter. King Edward III began this order sometime in the 1340s. Members wear a blue garter of cloth around their sleeves, on which is written *"Honi soit qui mal y pense."* This is the motto of the Order of the Garter.

Why did the best knights in England choose a garter as their symbol—and what does the motto mean? The secret of the knights is hidden back in time. You must travel back six centuries to find it, but to do so you will first have to become a knight yourself!

 To activate the Time Machine, turn the page.

**TIME TRAVEL
ACTIVATED.
Stand by for Equipment.**

EQUIPMENT

For your mission, you will take with you a simple peasant's outfit. You will be wearing it when you arrive in the age of knights.

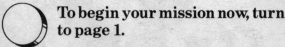

To begin your mission now, turn to page 1.

To learn more about the time to which you will be traveling, turn to the next page.

DATA BANK

These facts about knights and medieval England will help you to complete your mission:

1) Knights preferred to fight on horseback rather than on foot. They used swords, spears, lances, and many kinds of metal and wooden clubs.

2) Knights often fought mock battles called tournaments for sport. They used long lances to try and knock their opponents off their horses.

3) Knights wore metal armor for protection in tournaments and battle. A suit of armor was called a harness.

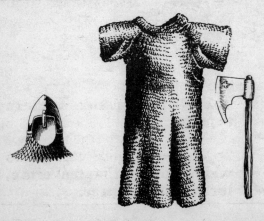

4) Two kinds of bow and arrow were used in battles in the 1300s. The crossbow was very powerful but slow. The string had to be pulled by a complicated little machine. The longbow was much faster but tricky to use. The longbow was a new weapon, and only the English knew how to use it.

5) Knights never used bow and arrow. They preferred their swords and looked down on the archers who accompanied them in battle.

6) Though gunpowder was used in Europe as early as 1300, it was not until the 1400s that guns were safe enough or powerful enough to be important in fighting.

7) In the Middle Ages, criminals could find sanctuary in churches and cathedrals. It was forbidden to pursue them there.

8) Young men learning to become craftsmen or tradesmen were called apprentices. Apprentice knights were called squires. A squire could only become a knight in a ceremony performed by a king or prince.

9) Knights had a code of honor called chivalry. A knight swore to be brave, generous, and loyal to his lord, and to protect and honor women.

10) People accused of being witches or sorcerers in the Middle Ages were often tied up with ropes and thrown into a pond. If the person floated, he or she was supposed to be guilty. If they sank, they were judged innocent. If they were found guilty, they were often burned at the stake.

11) King Edward III ruled England from 1327 to 1377. One of his most famous victories was the

Europe About 1360

battle of Crecy, fought in northern France in 1346.

12) Edward III's son Edward, called the Black Prince because of the color of the armor he wore at Crecy, never became king, because he died before his father did. He married Lady Joan of Kent in 1361. Their son Richard became king in 1377.

13) Each knight wore a family design on his shield, clothes, and armor to identify him in battle. These heraldic designs were passed down from one generation to another in noble families.

14) The kings and princes of England wore a heraldic design, or crest, of three gold leopards on a red background. The kings of France wore a crest of lily flowers.

15) The famous King Arthur may not have been a king at all. We don't even know if that was his real name. All that is really known about him is that he led one of the native tribes of Britons against the invading tribes of Angles and Saxons in the fifth century A.D.

16) Centuries after the real Arthur died, stories about him were told and retold. Each time the story was retold it got a little better, until it became the elaborate legend we hear about today. The stories of the search for the Holy Grail and the Knights of the Round Table, for example, were invented in the twelfth century, seven hundred years after Arthur died.

17) The Black Death was one name for a terrible plague, or disease, that killed almost one third of the people in Europe in the 1340s. It was

spread by rats and fleas, though nobody knew that at the time.

18) The Black Death arrived in England in late 1348. It disappeared in winter, because the cold kept the fleas from spreading it, but it swept the country in the warm months of 1349.

19) Medieval towns were usually surrounded by high walls for protection against attack. An attack on a town was called an assault or siege. Armies besieging a town sometimes used giant catapults to throw rocks against the walls.

20) The English kings had a castle in the town of Windsor from the late 1000s on. Winchester, about forty miles from Windsor, was the capital of England during Saxon times and was still a very important city in the 1300s.

```
DATA BANK
COMPLETED.
TURN THE PAGE TO
BEGIN YOUR MISSION.
```

 Don't forget, when you see this symbol, you can check the Data File in the back of the book for a hint.

ou're standing on a dirt road lined with trees near Windsor, England. It's April 28, 1344. In the distance you can see a castle on a hill, with giant tents on the fields below.

You can hear the sound of galloping hooves coming up behind you.

You spin around. A big horse rears back on its hind legs. Its front hooves kick wildly in the air.

"Easy, Bizan!" says its rider. He's dressed like a knight!

The horse neighs and snorts with surprise at your sudden appearance. You jump out of the way, but the panicked horse throws the knight into the weeds by the side of the road.

"Oof!" says the knight. His heavy armor makes a clanking sound as he falls flat on his back. On the road behind him, a boy leading a horse turns and runs away. The two horses trot off to graze in a field.

"Squire!" calls the knight in a weak voice. "Squire Randall! Where is that boy?"

You walk over to the knight. "May I help you, sir?" you say.

"By all the blessed saints' toenails! Yes!" You pull him to his feet. The armor clicks and clanks as the knight moves. "Nothing broken, thanks be to the Blessed One," he says. "And thanks be to you, my young friend. Tell me— did you see the wizard?"

"Uh, no," you say. "What wizard?"

"As I rode, a magnificent wizard, with wings of purple, appeared in my path. My horse leaped like he had seen a demon! I could not see the wizard well, because the visor in my helmet is very narrow. But I tell you, it was amazing!"

A wizard? Demon? What's amazing, you think as you help the knight catch the horses, is his imagination. That was *you* on the road— and you don't have purple wings!

"This is a sign of bad luck," continues the knight as he leads his horse back to the road. "For such a thing to happen on my first prac- tice ride of the day, ill fate must await me at King Edward's tournament. Are you going to watch us fight?"

A tournament! There will be many knights there, perhaps including some who wear the garter. You tell him yes.

"Come with me, then," says the knight. "My name is Sir Cuthbert."

"Don't do it, Sir Cuthbert!" a voice cries. A boy about fourteen years old jumps out from behind a tree.

"So there you are," shouts Sir Cuthbert,

"you lazy, cowardly good-for-nothing! Squire Randall, why hide you there?"

"I too beheld the wizard," says Randall. "It looked just as you have said. But swiftly it transformed itself, with evil magic—into this creature here!" He points an accusing finger at you.

Sir Cuthbert looks at you a moment. Then he scowls and hits his squire on the ear. "Enough of your lies, scoundrel! Where were you to help me rise? I had to accept the aid of a kind stranger. And now you accuse this same kind person of witchcraft! You dare call yourself my squire? Someday I'll beat some sense into you! Come along, both of you!"

 Turn to page 15.

You're in a deserted, narrow street in the city of Winchester. It's May 20, 1357.

You hear cheering in the distance, and the sound of trumpets.

You turn into the main square of the city, in front of a half-built cathedral. "Hurrah for the prince!" people shout. You're almost trampled by a wildly cheering crowd.

It's a parade! Knights on horseback push slowly through the crowd. Colorful banners fly everywhere. A string of flowers hits you on the head, and you look up. What look like giant birdcages hang from poles above a row of shops. Beautiful girls stand inside the cages, throwing flowers.

There's a man in a short green coat standing next to you, and a boy in a thick leather apron. "What's going on?" you ask.

The man in green looks at you with surprise. "You mean you do not know? That's Prince Edward, the king's eldest son. He brings a prisoner from the war in France. Not just any prisoner—it's John, the King of France himself."

A tall, blond man about thirty years old waves to the crowd. That must be the prince, you decide. He wears a long tunic with some sort of cat design on it, and—yes! Around his arm is a *dark blue garter*. Some of the knights with him wear the same thing. The garter you're looking for is dark blue. Of course! The Order of the Garter exists. Now, in 1357!

"Why do they wear those garters on their sleeves?" you ask the boy in the leather apron.

"I'm damned if I know," he says. "Seems foolish to me. I'm apprentice to a harness maker, so I see them often enough. But only certain knights wear them."

"It's the knights that fought with the prince at the battle of Crecy," says the man in green. "Only they can wear the garter. I know, because I was there! I'm a yeoman farmer, but I was one of the king's archers at Crecy. Those were the days! It was the archers won the battle, but the knights who rode off with all the glory!"

"Ah, get off, Yeoman Tom," says the boy. "Ye're always puffin' yerself and yer bows and arrows."

So this man fought with the prince at the famous Battle of Crecy! "Do you know what the motto means," you ask, *"Honi soit qui mal y pense?"*

"You got me over a barrel," says Tom. "It's French, is all I know. I don't speak French, but I think *mal* means 'evil.'"

The crowd surges forward. You barely have room to breathe! A man in a black robe trimmed with fur rides just behind the prince. He doesn't look as happy as everyone else. He must be the captured King of France.

The man who fought with Edward at Crecy looks closely at you. "Say, I've not seen you before. Traveling, are you? Looking for work?"

"Uh, yes," you say.

"Well, friend, you've come to the right place! Ever since 1349, we've had work for any pair of hands that can hold a hoe. So many people died that year, in the Great Death, that plenty of good work has gone a-begging since. Come along with me!"

"*My* master needs another apprentice," says the boy in the leather apron. "Ye can find me down on Hastings Street if ye'd rather learn to be a harness maker."

Taking a job is not a bad idea, you think. It looks like you're in the correct time period. Now you have to find a way to get to know some knights. Which of these two opportunities will bring you closer to your goal?

Stay in the same time and join the yeoman on the manor farm. Turn to page 13.

Stay in the same time and become apprentice to a harness maker. Turn to page 23.

You're sitting in the harness maker's shop, surrounded by half-finished leg pieces, breast pieces and shields. You've been working for a week now. In the little spare time you have, Richard has been teaching you more about fighting with quarterstaves.

"Keep those bellows pumping!" shouts the master.

Sweat runs down your face. Your job is to keep a red-hot fire going. You push up and down with your foot on a big windbag. The workmen hammer on the sheets of glowing metal, sending sparks flying everywhere. A spark lands in your hair! You brush it out with your hand. Out of the corner of your eye, you see somebody enter the shop.

"Welcome, good Sir Nigel!" says the master. Finally, a knight has arrived to pick up a suit of armor. He's about twenty-five years old and wears a *dark blue garter* around his arm! That's just what you've been looking for.

"Here it is," the master says proudly, holding out a new shield. You help Sir Nigel into

his armor, holding the different pieces so he can slip them on.

Nigel takes a few steps around the room. "The joints are a mite stiff," he says. His voice sounds funny, echoing inside the helmet. "But I am pleased."

As you help Sir Nigel take his armor off, he looks at you.

"A strange thing," he says. "You much resemble an old friend of mine. But you're too young to have been with us at Crecy, are you not?"

"Crecy?" you say.

"Surely you've heard of Crecy, the battle famous!" He taps the garter on his arm. "*Honi soit qui mal y pense.* We were all there. Evil to those . . ."

"That will be enough, apprentice!" your master says. "Return to your work!" Sir Nigel and his servants carry the armor away.

The famous motto! You've found a knight who might know about it. But he is walking out the door! Time to make your move, you think as you hold a red-hot piece of iron in the fire. Why not run after Sir Nigel and ask him what it means?

"Watch what ye're doing, idiot!" your master shouts. Startled, you pull the iron out of the flames. As you do, you knock over a tub full of metal-eating acid. You jump out of the way as it pours across the floor.

"You fool!" shouts the master, hitting you over the head with a stick.

You throw off your leather apron. "I'm leaving," you say.

"Leave?" the master roars. "You cannot leave. You're mine, worthless as you are, for seven long years. Do you know what we do to apprentices who run away?" He holds a red-hot piece of steel in front of you. "We brand them on the forehead with this!"

The door is right behind you. "Look!" you say, pointing over the master's shoulder. He turns for a moment, and you run out the door.

"After the runaway!" the master shouts. "Don't let the devil get away!"

The street is full of horses, carts, and people. You run as fast as you can, but the men chasing you are familiar with these streets. You can't see Sir Nigel anywhere. Where would he have gone?

The cathedral lies ahead of you, on the left. To your right is a guildhall, a big building where the cloth merchants meet. It might be full of people, if you're lucky, and places to hide.

The men are almost at your heels! Where should you hide?

 Hide in the cathedral. Turn to page 20.

 Hide in the guildhall. Turn to page 33.

You're walking in a field under the hot sun. Tom, your yeoman-farmer friend, walks up ahead. He steers a wooden plough pulled along by an ox. The plough rips a long groove called a furrow through the soil.

A basket full of seeds hangs from your neck. You dip your hand in the basket and plant seeds in the furrow as you walk along.

"Yeoman Tom!" shouts a man by the edge of the road.

Tom pulls on the ox's reins to make it stop. "Bah!" he says. "Here comes the bailiff. Just when I thought we'd get a good day's work done!"

"Who's the bailiff?" you ask.

"He's the one who runs the manor for Sir Quentin, the knight who calls himself lord around here."

The bailiff looks at you with curiosity as he approaches.

"So, Tom," he says, pointing at you, "you're doing well enough now to hire a landless laborer!"

"And why shouldn't I?" says Tom. "No serf am I, anymore. I don't work for Sir Quentin. I'm a free yeoman, I am! I won my freedom fighting for the king at Crecy."

"Yes, I know, Tom. We're all very proud of you. But Sir Quentin's fields need ploughing, too, and your family has always done it for him. Take your ox and your new worker and spend the rest of the day there." The bailiff turns and walks away.

Tom picks up a clod of dirt and starts to throw it at the bailiff. You grab his hand to stop him.

"He can't command me like that!" Tom growls. "If Sir Quentin wants me to work his fields instead of my own, he'll have to pay me, he will. I've had quite enough of knights looking down on me. Come on. We'll show him! We'll spend the rest of the day shooting arrows."

You follow Tom back to his cottage. He picks up a quiver of arrows and a big bow almost as tall as he is. "Come on!" he says to you. "The boys await us down on the village green!"

You follow him. It might be useful to learn archery, you think.

You haven't learned much about knights working here as a farmer, though. Perhaps you should have gone with the harness maker's apprentice, instead. You could sneak off and jump back in time to meet him. Should you?

 Jump to Winchester and work for the harness maker. Turn to page 23.

 Stay with Tom and learn how to use a longbow. Turn to page 45.

You're sitting at the edge of the field below the walls of Windsor Castle. Knights come out of big tents topped with colored banners flying in the wind. Squires help the knights mount their horses. Queen Philippa of England and other nobles sit on a raised platform in the shade. Everyone else sits on logs or in the grass.

Trumpets blow. Drummers drum. The first event at King Edward's tournament is about to begin!

King Edward leads a team of nineteen other knights against a team of challengers led by Sir Miles Stapleton. The knights are covered in armor from head to toe. Even their horses wear armor. They form two lines facing each other, thirty yards apart.

The queen stands up and holds a handkerchief in the air.

"Let the battle begin!" she cries, and drops the handkerchief. When it hits the ground, the knights spur their horses on.

"My sword, and St. George!" they shout as they ride. You can feel the ground tremble as the forty horses gallop faster and faster.

The chargers meet, right in front of you, in a crash of splintering lances and smashing bodies. Three of the horsemen are knocked completely off their saddles. Their squires run to help them up. The rest spin their horses around to charge again. And again! Soon there are only a few knights left on horseback. Squires lead the horses away, and the knights continue the combat on foot.

"Who is your champion today, Lady Joan?" says one of two women sitting near you.

"I have sworn not to tell his name," replies the other, a blond girl about sixteen years old. "But he is a right chivalrous knight. I have given him my garter."

A garter! That's part of what you're here to find: the meaning of the message on a garter!

"Excuse me," you say, "is your knight friend a member of the Order of the Garter?"

The women look at each other, then at you.

"Order of the Garter? Whatever can you mean?" says Lady Joan. "I have given him an item of my clothing as a token of my affection. As you see, all the knights are wearing favors of the ladies they love."

She's right. Almost all the knights have a lady's glove, veil, or garter tied around their lance or armor. But if they haven't heard of the Order of the Garter, maybe you've arrived too early in time.

"Watch out!" someone calls, as a pair of grappling knights almost falls on top of you. Lady Joan and her friend pick up their skirts and slip away.

This tournament-fighting is serious business. You decide to cross behind a tent to the other side of the field, where it looks a little safer.

"Halt!" a voice calls. It's Randall, the squire who saw your jump in time. He's pointing a long sword straight at you! "You're a sorcerer, and I know it," he snarls. "I challenge you to a fight!"

"I don't want to fight," you say, "and I'm not a sorcerer."

"Not only a sorcerer, but a coward!" he sneers. "Come on, choose your weapon. Swords or quarterstaves?"

You know he can kill you if you try to fight with swords, so you ask for the other. But what is it?

"Quarterstaves it is," he says. "On your honor, wait right here, and I'll get them." He runs off.

No matter what quarterstaves are, you think, he's bound to be trained in how to use them. You're not! The Order of the Garter doesn't exist yet, so why stay here? If you jump to the future, you won't have to face Randall when he gets back.

 Jump five years ahead to 1349. Turn to page 27.

 Leap thirteen years to 1357. Turn to page 5.

20

You run into Winchester Cathedral, which is being enlarged.

Carpenters and masons are hard at work.

A hand tugs at your sleeve. "Please, a few coins for a poor beggar?" A raggedly dressed fellow is standing right behind you.

"I'm a runaway apprentice. My master hit me, so I came in here for sanctuary. He can't come in here to get me, but that was three years ago! Now I can't leave the cathedral, or he'll brand me."

Here's someone else who sought sanctuary in the cathedral! According to medieval law, you're safe inside the cathedral—but only if you don't go out again. Lucky you don't have to stay. You find a quiet chapel, to jump in time. Where to?

There were lots of knights in the prince's procession, you remember. Why not try to talk with them?

 Turn to page 34.

ou're standing in an alleyway in Windsor, May 15, 1349. A cart rolls through the street, loaded with bodies. The plague is raging! Of course—you should have known better. It arrived in England *last* year, in 1348. People were safe all winter because of the cold, but when it got warmer in the spring the rats and fleas started spreading the disease again.

You hear music coming from the direction of the public square. You look out.

What a strange sight! The square is full of people dancing.

A girl comes out of the crowd. "I have been dancing for two days," she says. "If we never stop dancing, we will not catch the plague."

Oh, this is sad. They hope that dancing will protect them from disease! You back away.

You'd better retrace your steps. You wander down the street, looking for a place to jump in time without being seen.

Turn to page 15.

ou're walking through the crowded streets of Winchester. You're looking for the harness maker's shop. You remember that in this time period harness is another word for a suit of armor. You might talk to some knights at a harness shop, when they come to buy armor!

The main street of Winchester is paved with round stones. Down the middle and along the sides are gutters full of all sorts of garbage. It stinks! The gutters are open, flowing sewers. It will be centuries before modern plumbing is invented.

"*Gardyloo!*" shouts a woman in a window of one of the gingerbread houses. You jump out of the way just in time, as she dumps a pail full of watery garbage right into the street.

"Watch where you're throwing that!" you say.

The woman stares down at you. "Watch out yourself," she snaps. "I warned you, gardyloo!"

That must mean "beware of the garbage," you decide. You watch the houses above you as you walk, looking for people about to dump their trash.

"You there!" someone shouts. "Do ye still want a job?"

It's the harness maker's apprentice. He's playing with a friend, fighting with long wooden poles.

"I'm interested," you reply.

"Wait here with me," the apprentice says. "The master's not returned yet from the prince's parade. Here!" He tosses you one of the wooden poles. "Let's play at quarterstaves."

So that's what a quarterstaff is! You hold your quarterstaff the way he does, with one hand at the middle and the other to one side. He tries to hit you with the end of the stick. You block him with yours and push him away.

"Fairly done," he says. Then he swings the pole around quickly and knocks you to the ground.

"Hah!" he laughs while helping you up. "I can teach ye a thing or two! My name's Richard."

You tell him your name and shake his hand. He proceeds to show you how to win at quarterstaves.

"So *there* you are!" a loud voice bellows. A big bald man in a leather apron slaps Richard on the side of the head. "I said you were free for a half holiday, not a whole holy week! Back to the shop with you!"

Richard rubs his head and looks up. "I know, sir. But look! I've found ye a new apprentice."

The harness maker rubs his chin as he looks you over. "So you want to be a harness maker, eh? It will mean hard work, from sunup to sundown, six days a week except holy days. But as sure as day follows night, after seven years of apprenticeship you'll know all about making armor. Then you'll be free to go off and make your fortune as you see fit."

Seven years! You don't want to stay here that long, but you don't want to lie to him. What can you say?

"As long as day follows night," you tell him, "I will work for you." That's not promising anything, for a time traveler. For you, day doesn't always follow night!

 Become a harness maker on page 9.

26

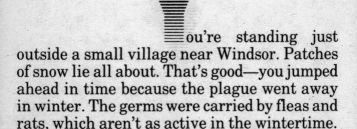

ou're standing just outside a small village near Windsor. Patches of snow lie all about. That's good—you jumped ahead in time because the plague went away in winter. The germs were carried by fleas and rats, which aren't as active in the wintertime.

You walk down the main street of the village. Where is everybody? The houses look empty, deserted.

This is a ghost town! Did the plague leave nothing alive here at all? Maybe you should jump further ahead in time.

Something moves in a doorway. It's only a dog, slinking along the side of a house. The poor dog is thin. Its eyes are wild.

"Awroo!" There's another dog behind you. And another up ahead. You're surrounded by a pack of dogs, growling and drooling with hunger! They've found something unusual: nice, fat prey. You!

One of the dogs trots forward, baring its fangs. But he's going to have to find his dinner somewhere else!

Jump ahead 7 years. Turn to page 5.

You're standing in a narrow street in the town below Windsor Castle. It's September 15, 1349. All the doors and windows you see are shut. There's nobody around, and an awful smell hangs in the air. A wooden cart pulled by a hungry-looking ox turns the corner. Two men in long robes with dark hoods walk beside it.

"Bring out your dead!" they shout. "Bring out your dead!"

One of the doors opens, and two weeping girls pull something wrapped in a blanket out into the street. The blanket slips for a moment—it's a dead body! There's an ugly black lump under the dead woman's shoulder. Her white face is frozen in a look of horrible pain.

The *plague*! It's 1349. You've arrived smack in the middle of the Black Death, the worst disease in the history of the world.

The men toss the body onto the cart, which is full of other bodies. This is awful! So many people are dying at once that the people left alive can't even give them funerals.

You run down a side street to get away from the sight. You come to a wide public square.

A bony hand grips your arm.

"Saints' relics, at an unholy price," whispers an old man in a black hood. "Protection for your immortal soul—they will guarantee you a place in paradise! Only a few coins." He brings out a little box and opens it. "This is the finger of a blessed saint. Pardon for all your sins! We're all going to die. This is the end of the world! But you may choose: will you go to heaven, or to hell?"

"No, thanks," you say, trying not to look in the box.

He grips you tighter. "I don't know your face," he says. "From where did you come?"

"I'm . . . a visitor."

"A stranger!" He throws back his hood and calls to some people on the other side of the square. "Look here!" he cries. "A stranger among us! It may be one of the evil ones who have been poisoning the wells and killing us!"

More hands grab you.

"Let me go," you yell. "No one is poisoning the wells. That's not what's causing the plague!"

"Oho. So it's not the wells, but something else. And *you* know what it is! Of course you know, because you're causing it yourself!"

You jerk your arm from his grasp and run.

"Catch the stranger! The poisoner is getting away!"

You turn into an alley and catch your breath. Time to get out of here! But should you jump a few months ahead in time, or a few months back?

 Four months back in time. Turn to page 22.

 Four months ahead? Turn to page 26.

ou're being hauled off to the stocks! Across from the cathedral sits a row of big wooden structures, with holes in them. The men carrying you tip the top block of wood up and slip your head and legs through the carved holes set between the two halves.

Thunk! You're locked in! You squirm about, but the wood is tight around your neck and ankles.

All day long people laugh and throw things at you as they walk by. The angrier you get, the more they laugh. What a humiliating way to be punished! You could jump to another time, but according to the rules of Time Travel, you're supposed to avoid disappearing when people can see you, unless it's a matter of life or death. You wait until night falls, when no one is around, before you can leave.

Jump back in time to Winchester, 1357. Turn to page 23.

ou fall on stony ground. You can see your horse, grazing up ahead, with the empty pieces of armor slumped across the saddle.

There's a crowd of people gathered around the horse. They stare at you.

"A sorcerer!" they cry. "First there was someone riding in the armor on the horse. Then, by magic, the armor was empty! Now the sorcerer has reappeared!"

You get up and try to run, but they chase you down and grab you.

"Take the magician to the dungeon," someone says. "The priests will know what to do!"

Turn to page 42.

ou run into the guild-hall. It's a big stone building with long walls covered with tapestries.

Unfortunately, there's no crowd here for you to hide in. A few young men bat a ball around with flat, threaded mallets that look like primitive tennis rackets.

"There ye are," says a voice. You turn to run, but the harness maker's men grab your arms.

"Pardon us," they say as they drag you out, "the king forbids apprentices to run away. We'll try to keep the master from branding ye. But ye must be punished. Ye're going to spend a night and a day in the stocks!"

Turn to page 30.

ou're in the same quiet chapel of Winchester Cathedral, one week earlier. It's May 20 again. No one is hammering or climbing the long ladders today. Everyone must be outside, where you can hear the crowd cheering Prince Edward and his prisoner, King John.

You go out and follow the procession. The knights get down from their horses and enter the cloth merchants' guildhall across the way. You try to follow them in, but a guard pushes you back.

"Where think ye that ye're going?" he roars. He waves his sword in the air. "Stand back!"

A crowd of beggars tries to get in, too. "Please!" they beg. "A few coins for the poor!"

The door of the hall is pulled back. A man in a fur-lined coat comes out.

"A few coins?" he says to the beggars. "A lucky dozen of you will get more than that. As is the custom, the prince has ordered that twelve poor people be invited to share in his banquet, to represent the twelve apostles at the Last Supper." He points to a one-armed beggar. "You," he says, "and you, and you . . . and you." He's pointing at you!

You enter a large torchlit hall and find a seat at a very long wooden table next to a man dressed in silk and fur. Servants carry in huge trays with roast geese and pigs. The beggars stare at the food, eyes wide, as if they can't believe it's real.

There's a wooden plate in front of you, and a bowl, but no spoons, forks, or napkins. How are you going to eat without a fork?

The prince rises. "By the grace of God, heavenly provider, let the feast begin!" He picks up a piece of meat with his fingers and stuffs it in his mouth.

Everyone else digs in, too. Sometimes they use a piece of bread to slop up their gravy, but mostly they eat with their fingers. You've never seen a more complete display of poor table manners. And these are the rich people!

Since there are no utensils, you do as they do. Soon your fingers are all greasy.

"Dirty fingers, my young friend?" asks the man sitting next to you. "I'll show you what to do." He looks under the table, and whistles. A big, furry dog trots up. He gives the dog a scrap of meat, and wipes his fingers on the dog's fur.

He's using a dog for a napkin! Well, you wonder, what do they do for a handkerchief?

The man next to you laughs at your expression. "What ails you?" he says. "That's how it's done at banquets in all the world. I know. I'm a wanderer. Froissart is my name. I go from court to court, telling stories about the knights and kings of many lands. Some day I shall collect them all in a book."

"Say, maybe you can help me," you whisper. "I've been wondering about the garters those knights have on their sleeves."

"Ah, yes," says Froissart. "The knights of

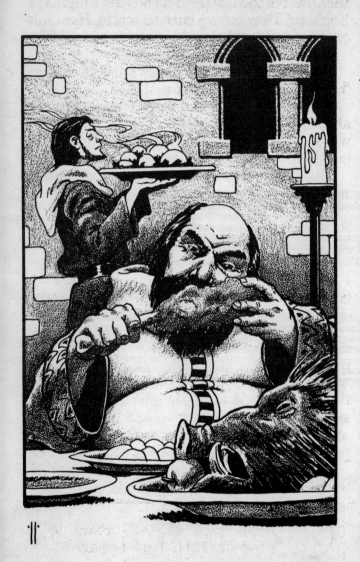

the Order of the Garter. The noblest knights of England! They have a curious motto, *Honi soit qui mal y pense.*"

"Do you know what it means?"

"I know the sense of the words, of course. 'Evil to those who think evil of it.'"

At last! You've found someone who knows about the famous motto! But—what do the words really mean? Evil to *whom*, who thinks evil of *what*? You ask Froissart.

"I'm afraid I cannot help you there. Only King Edward himself may really know the answer. He started the Order of the Garter—I think it was at the end of a tournament at Windsor in 1344."

Windsor, in 1344? You went to a tournament at Windsor, in that year, when you first got here! Only you saw the *first* day of a three-day tournament. If Froissart is right, you should go there at its *end*. The king knows the meaning of the motto, and the king could make you a knight.

The banquet is nearly over. The beggars at the end of the table are sitting back, grinning, after the best meal they've had in years.

"Thank you very much, Mr. Froissart," you say, "I must be going now."

You find an empty side room at the back of the hall.

 Jump back thirteen years to Windsor, 1344. Turn to page 61.

You decide to duel with Randall to prove you aren't a sorcerer. No true knight would turn down a challenge like that, and you are supposed to become a knight!

Randall tosses you a quarterstaff. You know how to use it. You also know that trial by water could have lead to your death by drowning.

A crowd gathers around you, including Sir Cuthbert. A blond boy about fourteen years old looks on with amusement.

"On your guard!" shouts Randall. He swings his pole straight at your head!

You duck the flying staff. Randall's too confident. He's left himself wide open! You jab the end of your staff right in his stomach.

"Oof!" he says, landing on his back.

The crowd around you laughs. "Well done!" shouts the blond boy.

Randall lurches to his feet and charges you. You block his swing, then the next. He is strong. Richard taught you, though, that strength is only a small part of the game. Fast reflexes and skillful footwork will beat brute strength every time.

You notice a pattern in the way Randall moves. When he jumps ahead with his left foot, he almost always is about to swing the long end of his pole up high and down on your head.

The next time he does it, you know what to do. You leap to the right and swing your quarterstaff sideways.

Your blow knocks Randall to the ground. The crowd around you cheers.

Randall's angry now. He jumps up, running straight at you with his pole out like a sword!

You step neatly to the side and smack him on the rear. Everyone laughs. An angry opponent, you know, is a weak opponent. You have to keep a cool head.

Randall's easy to beat, now. You land a hard blow on his stomach, and he falls down, breathless.

"Well fought!" one of the knights cries. "So brave a fighter could not be a sorcerer."

The blond boy claps you on the shoulder and leads you away, as Sir Cuthbert helps Randall up. "A well-fought and courageous game. Where are you from? I don't think I know you." He wears a red tunic with three gold leopards or lions embroidered on it.

"I'm a visitor," you say. "From far away."

"Be you noble or varlet?"

Now, that's a tricky question. He wants to know if you're a nobleman or not!

"I come from a land," you say vaguely,

"where all of us are noble."

He smiles. "By my word! You speak well of your native land. I can tell you are of noble education by your proud speech."

"My lord," says a knight, "perhaps this is the new squire we expected from the kingdom of Navarre."

Navarre? You can't tell them where you're *really* from. Why not let them believe you're from a place far away, as Navarre seems to be?

"My courageous friend from Navarre," says the blond boy, "will you join my service as a squire?"

You're delighted, but surprised. He isn't any older than most squires himself! You'll have to become a squire before you can become a knight, but should you accept his offer? Or wait and try to become a squire to one of the other, older knights?

Tell the blond boy yes. Turn to page 49.

Tell him no. Turn to page 51.

A guard takes you to the castle to await your trial on the charge of being a sorcerer. You enter the castle through a thick oak door. You brush against the cold, damp stone walls of a dark tunnel. A man appears, dressed in black. He holds a flickering torch.

He takes you down a steep stone staircase. In the dim torchlight you see a row of cells with doors made of iron bars. The man unlocks one of the doors and shoves you inside. He picks up a thick chain attached to a ring in the wall and locks it with a click on your leg.

You're locked in a dungeon!

"Psst!" someone whispers. You go to the iron door.

"What year is it?" a hoarse voice calls.

"It's 1344," you tell him. "How long have you been here?"

"I don't know!" the voice wails. "They've forgotten me. I've forgotten why they put me here!"

You made a mistake in getting locked up this way, you think, but the answer to the riddle of the motto may still be in this time.

You wait in the damp dungeon cell, trying to think of a way to escape. A knight should be brave, after all, and you should act like one if you want to become one.

44

You hear the guard coming. You flatten yourself against the damp cell wall, ready to push off when the door opens.

Only you hear *two* voices coming down the tunnel. They've come to take you to your trial!

The guards drag you back outside. Three priests in long black robes take you to the edge of a pond. They tie your hands behind your back and bind your feet together.

"Prisoner," says the head priest, "you stand accused of witchcraft. By the ancient test, you will be thrown into the water. If you float, we will know you are a sorcerer. Then you will be burned at the stake. If you are innocent, you will sink!"

This trial by water is crazy! What good is it to prove you're innocent if the proof makes you drown?

Two priests carry you to a rock above the water. You take a deep breath. They swing you back and forth and fling you into the pond!

You land in the cold water. You struggle to get free, but the ropes on your hand and feet are tightly tied.

You've had enough of this. You're not going to wait around to see if you sink.

 Jump ahead in time to 1349. Turn to page 27.

 Jump ahead to 1357. Turn to page 5.

ou're standing with yeoman Tom and a group of his friends on the village green. Geese wander about as the men shoot three-foot-long arrows at a target.

"Here," says Tom, "this bow's just your size. Stand like this, with your elbow pointed at the target. Hold your arrow fast against the string, and pull back."

You pull the string with all your strength, but it's very difficult. You worry about the arrow slipping off the string, but you hold on. When you just can't pull any harder, you let it go.

TWING! The arrow wobbles through the air and lands in the base of a tree just missing a goose.

"Ho ho!" laughs Tom. "Already collecting feathers for your arrows, eh?"

"Don't just pull with your arms," says another man. "Use your entire body. Like this."

TWANG! His arrow lands dead center.

"Good shot!" cries another man. "I'll give a tankard of ale to anyone who can shoot one better!"

Tom whips out an arrow, pulls, and in a flash it's gone. The second arrow slices the first one in two!

The men cheer. Tom drinks down his ale.

"Let's go a-roving, boys!" he roars.

You follow the men down the road toward Winchester. You stay out of their way as they shoot arrows at trees, birds, cats, and anything else that seems like a target.

They're still shooting arrows when you arrive at the gates of Winchester. Like most big towns, Winchester is surrounded by a high wall with a big arched gate in the middle. But there's something terrible above this gate: a row of skulls stuck up on wooden spikes!

"What are those doing up there?" you ask Tom.

"Ho! Those are some fellows who just lost their heads, aren't they?" he laughs. "Rogues and criminals, they were. The Lord Mayor of Winchester had them put up there as a warning. Anyone coming through these walls had better behave."

"They make a nice target, don't they," says one of Tom's friends. "Let's see if I can hit one!"

He pulls out an arrow and takes aim at one of the grisly things. The arrow zips up and over the wall.

Two angry guards come running out of the gate, followed by a man dressed in silk and furs. Tom's friend's arrow is stuck through his hat!

"Who dared shoot an arrow through the Lord Mayor's hat?" the men shout. Your friends look at their feet. The guards look at you!

"All right, young troublemaker," says one of them. "You're going to spend a night and a day in the stocks!"

 Turn to page 30.

ou take another look at the blond boy's tunic as Randall limps away. The tunic bears the leopard emblem of English royalty. This must be Edward, the Black Prince, whom you saw as a grown man in Winchester in 1357! Though he's young, he's the king's son and he already commands many knights.

"To serve you will be an honor," you tell him. You start to kneel, but Edward takes your hand and pulls you up.

"No need for formality, brave squire of Navarre," says the prince. He calls to another boy. "This is Nigel, squire to one of my best knights, Sir John Chandos. Nigel, I want you to train our new squire."

Nigel bows and kisses the prince's hand. "As you command, my lord," he says.

You follow Nigel and the prince. You join a crowd of knights and ladies gathering on a nearby hill around King Edward III. The king waves his hand, and instantly the crowd falls silent.

"Many years ago," he shouts, "according to the stories, the glorious King Arthur used to meet on this very hill with his Knights of the

Round Table. The best knights of his kingdom would sit in a circle, so that no one knight could say that he sat at the head of the table."

"We hereby swear, on our honor as a knight and king, that before four years have passed we will start a new Round Table. The best knights of our kingdom will sit with us here, in a chapel we will dedicate to the holy knight, St. George!"

"Hurrah!" cry the knights and ladies. The knights wave their swords in the air. "Hurrah for King Edward! Hurrah for the new Round Table!"

Well, the king's plans for "the best knights of our kingdom" sound like the beginning of the order of knights you're looking for. But he didn't mention the garter, or the famous motto. Could Froissart have been wrong about the year he began the Order?

You take a close look at Nigel as he leads you off to the tents. You recognize him—he's the knight you saw in 1357 at the armorer's shop you were working in! He's still a squire now, but you know that someday he'll become Sir Nigel and wear the garter. He'll be the perfect person to teach you what knights need to know. Then, when the opportunity comes to become a knight yourself, you'll be ready for it!

Become a squire. Turn to page 53.

You decide you'd rather become a squire to a full-grown knight.

"Sorry," you tell the boy. "I have other plans."

The boy smiles in a strange way, and turns away.

Sir Cuthbert stares at you with astonishment. Squire Randall grins wickedly.

"What!" Cuthbert shouts. "You said no to the Prince of Wales? Edward, the king's son? You're crazy!"

Ow! Somebody hits you on the back of the head. "On your knees, fool!" an angry knight shouts.

"I . . . I'm sorry," you say, "I didn't know!" You look again at the tunic the boy is wearing. Of course, it has three gold leopards on it—and leopards decorate the crest of the English kings.

"Get out of here, idiot," the knights shout. They push you away.

You hide in the crowd of tournament spectators. Everyone is following a tall man in armor who strides to the top of the hill. The man looks like the prince—it must be King Edward III himself!

"Many years ago," the king shouts, "according to the stories, the glorious King Arthur used to meet on this very hill with his Knights of the Round Table. The best knights of his kingdom would sit in a circle, so that no one knight could say that he was best because he sat at the head of the table."

"We hereby swear, on our honor as a knight and king, that before four years have passed we will start a new Round Table. The best knights of our kingdom will sit with us here, in a chapel we will dedicate to the holy knight, St. George!"

"Hurrah!" cry the knights and ladies. "Hurrah for King Edward! Hurrah for the new Round Table!"

The king's plans for the "best knights of our kingdom" sound like the beginnings of the Order of the Garter. The king didn't mention the garter, though. If he's starting a *new* Round Table, why not go back to the time of the *old* one to see if King Arthur knows what the motto means?

It's no use staying here, in 1344, where everyone will soon know you refused the prince's offer.

Go back 1000 years to look for King Arthur. Turn to page 80.

You're standing on the training field at Windsor with a group of other squires.

"Here, take this lance," Nigel says. He's been training you for several days, but this is the first time you've used the real equipment. The lance is not as big as the long lances knights use, but it's heavy enough for you.

Nigel points at a strange T-shaped contraption. A target hangs from one end of the T, and a bag of sand from the other.

"That's a quintain," Nigel says. "We use it to practice our aim. Hold the lance steady, and keep it pointed at the middle of the target. If you don't hit it right in the middle, watch out!"

"Watch out for what?" you ask.

"You'll find out!" The other squires laugh.

You grip the lance tightly and run down the field. The point of the lance wobbles as you run. You hit the target a little to the left of center.

WHAM! The pole spins around, and the bag of sand smacks you in the back of the head! You go sprawling on the ground.

Everyone laughs.

You pick yourself up and laugh along with

them.

"Let me try that again!" you say.

"That's the spirit," says Nigel. "A brave knight never gives up!"

You try it over and over again. The back of your head hurts from being hit so often with the sandbag, but your aim is getting better.

"Let's try on armor next," says Nigel. "You're about my size, so my armor should fit you."

Here's your chance to feel what it's like to have armor on! You slip your legs into the leg

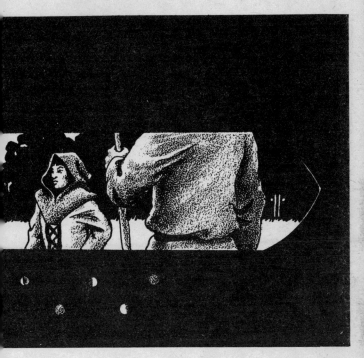

pieces and fit the breastplate on over your head. The arms are next, and finally the helmet.

You peer out at the world through the narrow helmet slit. You take a few steps, laughing at the clanking sound you make.

"Try getting up on a horse," Nigel says. He leads over a gray-and-white mare. "This is Rosalinde. Don't worry, she's a gentle horse. She always comes back to her stable eventually."

It's hard to get up on the horse while wearing the heavy armor. Nigel gives you a push, and you almost fall off the other side! Your helmet twists around. Now you can't see anything at all. You try to twist it back, but it won't move.

"What's wrong?" Nigel asks from below.

"My helmet's stuck!"

"Hey!" someone shouts. "Randall! What are you doing?"

Suddenly, your horse gives a whinny and gallops off. Randall must have scared it somehow!

You grab on tight to the horse's neck. The armor clanks and pinches as you bounce up and down. The horse is running at top speed!

"Watch where you're going, fool!" someone shouts.

"Sorry!" you call. There must be people watching your wild ride—but you *can't* watch where you're going. You can't even see!

"Rosalinde!" you call. "Slow down!" The horse gallops on.

Maybe you should jump in time. You could stay right here, but jump ahead a few minutes. Once you've disappeared out from inside this armor, you could catch the horse and walk it back.

 Jump ahead five minutes in time. Turn to page 32.

 Stay on the galloping horse. Turn to page 66.

Watch out!" Alison shouts. She pulls you out of the way, just as a horse races through the crowd. The horse pulls a cart driven by a laughing, drunken man.

"You'll rot in hell, carter!" Alison screams at him.

"Now," she says sweetly, "when you meet the king, you must be polite as a courtier. You must speak to him only when he speaks to you, understand?"

"All right," you say, as you enter a church full of dancing people. Just below the altar is a large wooden throne.

"Your majesty," Alison says, "a loyal subject wishes to ask you a question."

A nearly toothless one-eyed man sits grinning on the throne. His crown is tilted to one side, and he's hiccuping.

"Hic! Arise, my loyal subject," he says. He takes a big gulp of wine. "Off with their heads! Off with their shoes!"

Edward III is tall and blond, like the prince. Who is this, then?

"What kind of a king are you?" you ask.

"I? Hic! I am the Lord of Misrule. The King (hic) of Fools! My kingdom comes once a year, at Christmastime."

You hear a screech of laughter behind you. Alison is laughing so hard that tears run down her face.

"Wanted to meet the king, did ye? Ha ha! Well, here he is! Dear King Edward is still fighting his wars in France, so you'll have to make do with the King of Fools! Hoo hoo hoo!"

Well, you think as you sneak away, so King Edward isn't even in the country! He's in France. And Sir Walter de Manny, the most famous knight you've met yet, went to Brittany, which is also in France. If all the knights are going there, why not go to France yourself?

 Jump back a few months to find Edward at the battle of Crecy. Turn to page 74.

 Jump back a little further in time to find Sir Walter de Manny in Brittany. Turn to page 82.

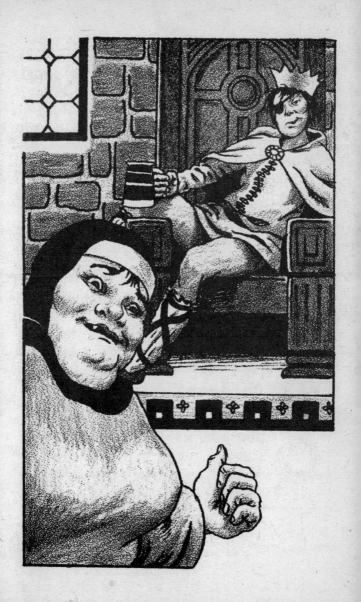

60

ou're standing in the streets of Windsor, late in the year 1346. Light snow lies on the ground, and music fills the air. People are dancing in the streets, spinning round and round with mistletoe and handkerchiefs swinging in their hands.

A big, red-faced woman says to you, "I've never seen you before, sweets.

"Why have you come here?"

"I'm looking for the king," you say.

"The king!" the woman grins. She has a gap between her two front teeth. "Well, now, this is your lucky day! I'm Alison, the fishwife. I happen to know the king very well, I do! Come along, love, come along! I'll introduce you!"

Could this woman really know the king? That would be lucky, if it were true. Only the king or prince can make you a knight, and King Edward, if anyone, must know what the motto on the garter means.

What kind of king will she come up with? You're curious and let her pull you along.

 Turn to page 57.

You're standing among the big tents on the tournament field below Windsor castle. It's April 30, 1344—two days after you first were here.

"You, there!" someone calls. It's Sir Cuthbert, the knight you met when you first arrived! He stands at the door to one of the tents, in the padded underclothes knights wear between their skin and their armor.

"Have you seen my lazy squire?" he asks. "If I don't get my armor on, I'll be late for the tournament! Do you know about armor?"

"Sure," you say, "I know all about it." Your week at the harness maker's shop is coming in handy after all. You help Sir Cuthbert into his armor and go with him to fetch his horse. Here you are acting in the place of a squire—you're on your way to becoming a knight!

"Do you see that knight over there with the blue cross on his shield?" says Sir Cuthbert as you help him mount his horse. "He's a French knight, called Sir Guy. He knocked me from my horse the last time we met. I swear on my sword, I will never cut my hair or take a bath until I vanquish him! Now, hand me my lance."

The long lance is so heavy you can barely carry it. Sir Cuthbert props it on his arm and joins the knights.

The queen signals for the fighting to begin, and the crowd cheers. Sir Cuthbert gallops for-

ward, pointing his lance at the French knight's shield.

CRAA-ACK! Sir Cuthbert's lance hits the shield head on, but splits in two! The French knight is knocked out of his saddle, but he stays on his horse.

They swing around to try again. This time, the French knight hits Sir Cuthbert on the helmet with his sword, and he tumbles off his horse.

You run out into the middle of the fighting and help Sir Cuthbert to his feet.

"I'm all right," he roars. "Get the horse off the field!" You grab the horse by the bridle and lead it off to the sidelines.

Sit Cuthbert and Sir Guy fight on foot. The French knight cracks Sir Cuthbert's shield in two and holds his sword against Sir Cuthbert's neck.

"Yield!" he shouts.

Sir Cuthbert yells and struggles, but the battle is over. "I yield," he finally says.

You run out on the field again and help him up. When he takes off his helmet, you see blood streaming down his face.

"Too bad," you say. "But it's only a game, after all. Better luck next time."

He glares at you. "Next time! That's the second good horse and harness that Frenchman has won from me."

The tournament game is more serious than you thought. In addition to the danger of getting hurt, the knights who lose have to give the winner their horses and armor.

64

You hear footsteps outside the door of the tent. Randall, Sir Cuthbert's squire, steps inside.

"You!" shouts the knight, hitting Randall with his armored hand. "Where have you been?"

Randall trembles, then he sees you. "It's this sorcerer's fault! I was bewitched, so I forgot what time it was. And you were bewitched, too. That's why you lost!"

Sir Cuthbert looks at you.

"Two days ago," Randall says, "I challenged this magician to a duel with quarterstaves. But then the sorcerer disappeared!"

Sir Cuthbert looks skeptically at Randall. "You've told this tale before, squire. I'm tired of it. There's a way to find out if you're right or not. Trial by duel!"

Randall smiles. "I have the quarterstaves right here. I'll wager this magician doesn't know how to use them!"

"Not so fast," Sir Cuthbert says, grabbing Randall by the arm. "The suspect should be allowed to choose. Will you face my squire with quarterstaves to prove you're not a sorcerer, or shall we submit you to the authorities for trial by water?"

 Fight a trial by combat.
Turn to page 38.

 Accept trial by water.
Turn to page 42.

ou're wet. You're wading in a shallow river, somewhere in Britain in the year A.D. 490. The water is stained red—is it blood?

Something floating in the river bumps into you from behind. It's a body, with a spear stuck through it!

A group of men on horseback crosses the river right next to you. You dive out of the way.

"Hold!" shouts a soldier, pointing a spear at your chest. "Be ye Angle, Saxon, or Briton?"

"None," you say. "I'm a . . . wanderer."

"A wandering bard?" He scratches his head. "There's nothing else ye could be. Come with me. General Artorius will want some entertainment tonight, to celebrate the British victory over the Saxons. You will perform for him. This way!"

Visit Artorius. Turn to page 78.

You hang on tight to the horse's neck as it gallops along. Nigel told you Rosalinde always returns to her stable. You hope he's right!

Your helmet is still stuck. It's scary to be riding so fast when you can't see anything! Soon, though, Rosalinde slows down.

You hear voices.

"Good horse, Rosalinde," someone says. That's Nigel's voice! "Well, did you enjoy your ride?"

"I would have enjoyed it better," you say, "if I had been able to see!"

He laughs and helps you down. He uses bear grease to get the helmet unstuck.

"That's enough practice for today," Nigel says. "Hurry out of that armor. Lady Joan of Kent has invited us on a hunting trip, and Sir Walter de Manny will be there."

Lady Joan is the young woman you met at Windsor when you first arrived in 1344, but who is Sir Walter de Manny?

"Sir Walter must be a brave knight," you say.

"Brave?" Nigel says with a laugh. "He's the bravest, most chivalrous knight in England. Many times he has captured an entire town with only a few knights to help him."

So you'll get to meet a famous knight! The closer you get to the bravest knights, you figure, the better your chances of becoming one yourself.

"If I become a knight," Nigel says with determination, "I'll be just like Sir Walter."

"But you're a squire," you say as you pull your leg out of the armor. "So someday you'll be a knight, right?"

"Not necessarily. Some people stay squire all their lives. I'll have to do very well as a squire, or prove my bravery on a battlefield. I've already been a squire for three years!"

Three years! Will it take *that* long for you to become a knight?

Go hunting with a famous knight. Turn to page 70.

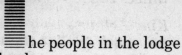he people in the lodge with you move restlessly.

"Play, bard!" roars Artorius. "Chant the story of a great king! Now!"

Luckily, you have an idea of what to play. You could chant something about King Arthur himself, work the motto into the words, and see what he says in response.

Oh, Arthur was a noble king,
He sat his warriors in a ring.
He said as long as they were able,
They'd be the knights of the Round Table.

Artorius takes a long swig from his mug, and wipes the foam from his beard.

"A round table, eh?" he says. "Sounds like a silly idea to me. It would have square bowls on it, I suppose!"

"Ho ho!" laugh his men.

What was the name of Arthur's best knight . . . Lancelot?

The luckiest knight was Lancelot . . .

You search desperately for a rhyme for Lancelot.

He practiced and prowled and pranced a lot.

"Ugh," growls Artorius, "this bard sings the worst rhymes I've ever heard!"

You'd better get the motto in here soon, you

think. You're running out of rhymes!

King Arthur took a double drink,
And said, "Evil to those who evil think"!

Artorius looks puzzled. "Evil to who? Who does what? Is there anyone here who knows what this bard is talking about?" He looks around at his friends, who shake their heads.

"Who was this king, anyway?" he asks you. "Where did he live?"

Brother! If this is the real Arthur, he isn't much like the stories told about him. He doesn't even recognize stories about himself!

He doesn't recognize the motto, either.

"Arthur was King of England," you say.

Artorius jumps to his feet.

"Angle-land! This bard is telling stories about the kings of our enemies, the Angles! What nerve!"

"Away with the fool!" shout the soldiers. They throw bones at you. The head of a fish hits you right on the forehead. You drop the harp and run for the door.

A crowd of laughing kids chases you into the woods. As soon as you're out of sight, you decide to jump in time. If Arthur doesn't know what the motto means, there's nothing more to find here. You'll have to go back to King Edward's time.

Jump ahead 850 years.
Turn to page 61.

You're walking through an overgrown field, holding half a dozen hunting dogs by the leash. Lady Joan rides on horseback. She wears a thick leather glove that covers her arm to her elbow.

Perched on the leather glove is a big black-and-gray spotted bird. It looks like a hawk of some sort.

"Why do you keep its head wrapped up?" you ask. Joan smiles. "This is a trained falcon. We will keep her hooded until we find something for her to chase." You watch Sir Walter de Manny.

"This will be our last hunt together for a while," he says to Lady Joan. "The king is sending me to France. The king's ally, the noble Countess of Brittany, is being attacked by the French army. I must go to her aid."

"You are a true and brave knight," says Joan. "When you hear of a lady in distress, off you go to help her, as the code of chivalry commands."

Suddenly, the dogs pull on the leashes you're holding.

"The dogs smell something," says Sir Walter. "Let them go!" They go bounding off, barking and growling.

Joan takes the hood off the falcon's head. "Quiet, my pretty one," says Joan. She gently strokes the falcon's feathers.

"I wonder," says Sir Walter with a smile, "what lucky knight's cheek the fair Lady Joan will stroke as gently as she strokes her falcon?"

Joan blushes. "I am in love with a knight, but I cannot tell his name. In days of old, when Lancelot joined King Arthur's Round Table, he and Queen Guinevere fell in love. They, too, kept their love a secret."

"Look there!" Nigel cries. The dogs are chasing long-necked, long-legged birds from a pond.

"Herons!" cries Joan. She strokes the falcon in a special way, points her curved beak toward the herons, and hurls her into the air. "Haie!" she shouts to the falcon. "Haie! Haie!"

In midair, the falcon slams into one of the herons with her claws. A spray of white feathers is knocked loose as the falcon brings the heron to the ground.

"Help me grab the heron," Nigel calls to you. "Watch out for its beak. It's as sharp as a dagger!"

You grab the big bird's feet, while Nigel holds its beak. It bleeds a little where the falcon held it with her claws, but otherwise it seems unharmed.

You carry the struggling bird to Sir Walter. He clips off the long plume of beautiful feathers at the back of its head and waves them in the air.

"Our first bird shall be a trophy-bird," Sir Walter says. "For luck, we will let it go." The heron flies away.

For several hours you play the same game over and over.

It will be a long time before you get to be a knight this way! Perhaps you should jump in time. It seems Froissart made an error when he told you that King Edward started the Order of the Garter here in 1344.

Edward just *talked* about starting a new Round Table, like the one King Arthur used to have. You heard him.

You could try jumping ahead a couple years, to see if the King has started the Order of the Garter by then. Or, if the order began with the king's plans for a new Round Table, perhaps the motto has something to do with the *old* Round Table. You could go back in time and ask King Arthur himself.

 Jump back 1000 years to look for King Arthur. Turn to page 80.

 Jump ahead two years to 1346. Turn to page 60.

It's August 26, 1346.

You're standing at the bottom of a grass-covered hill near the town of Crecy, France. An army of knights, archers, and foot soldiers waits at the top of the hill, while another army approaches across a field.

You can see big banners fluttering in the wind. The banners of the advancing army are blue, with yellow flower designs on them. The banners at the top of the hill are divided in four squares. Two of the squares have the same flower design; the others are red with what looks like golden lions on them.

One of these armies must be Edward and the English, and the other the French. Which should you join?

 Join the army on top of the hill. Turn to page 94.

 Join the army crossing the field. Turn to page 87.

You're standing near a river by a town of thatched-roof houses. There's a crowd of people coming your way, pulling something over a row of logs with long ropes.

"Heave!" shouts a guard, cracking a whip on the backs of the people pulling the ropes. You walk forward to see what it is they're dragging.

It's a ship! A long wooden ship, pointed at both ends.

"You!" shouts a man with a spear. "You're not a Saxon!" He pulls you over to the ship, and puts you to work pulling with the others. A whip cracks across your back.

"Heave!"

Next to you is a man with a tattoo on his cheek.

"What's going on?" you ask him.

"The Saxons are burying one of their kings," he mutters as he pulls. "They put all his weapons and jewels and magic powders in a ship with his body. They've made us dig a big hole, and now we're pulling the whole boat there to bury it!"

"Stop talking and pull, Welshman!" shouts the guard.

You keep quiet and pull.

"You're Welsh?" you ask the man when the guard goes away.

"I'm a Briton!" he says, "and proud of it! 'Welsh' is what the Saxons call 'foreigners.' For fifty years now the Anglo-Saxons have ruled here, but some day Arthur will come to lead the Britons once again!"

Ow! The guard's whip smacks across your back. Boy, does that sting!

Enough is enough! You run straight at the guard. He's surprised, caught off balance, and you knock him down. You keep running, heading for the forest where you won't be seen jumping in time.

You've been searching for Arthur, to ask him about King Edward's motto. But the man with the tattoo hoped Arthur would come *again*. . . . Of course! If Arthur lived at the end of the *fifth* century, that would mean the end of the 400s and beginning of the 500s. The 500s are the *sixth* century.

 **Jump back to A.D. 490.
Turn to page 65.**

You're sitting on a stool in a big one-room log house. Artorius, the leader of the Briton army, sits joking and drinking with his friends while a bard chants a poem. You don't know anything about being a bard, but you're the next performer!

You suspect that *Artorius* may be the real King *Arthur*! The two names are similar. Arthur was a Briton, and he was famous for winning battles against the invading Anglo-Saxons. If Artorius and Arthur are the same person, maybe he can tell you what the motto *"Evil to those who think evil of it"* means!

You listen to the bard chant a story about an old king named Geraint. Every once in a while he strums a couple of chords on a strange-looking little harp.

Men went to Catraeth, they were well renowned
From golden cups their mead they downed
For a year and a day they drank their fill
And then with a cry they charged up hill.
But of all who fought in that battle long
Only I came back, to sing this song.
Alas!

The bard finishes his story, and passes his harp to you.

"Good luck to you, whatever you sing," he whispers. "They're drunk as pigs and laugh at anything! Give them a song about a great king."

You pluck the strings of the harp. Everyone quiets down to listen to you.

You don't really have to play well, just sing and perform. But what words? What could you chant about that would help you on your mission?

 If you want to chant about a king, turn to page 68.

 If you don't, jump ahead 850 years and return to Edward's time. Turn to page 61.

You're standing in a small courtyard lined with white marble columns. You've traveled back a thousand years! It's A.D. 340.

You hear voices. Two men come your way, dressed in togas.

Togas! Where are you? This doesn't look like Britain at all. You jump through a dark doorway to hide.

You've jumped into a steaming hot pool!

"You! Come out of there, now!"

A man pokes a spear at you through the doorway. He wears a strange, curved helmet.

"This bath is reserved for Roman legionnaires!" he yells. "No Britons allowed!"

That explains it. You've come too far back, to the time when Britain was a colony of the Roman Empire! You swim to a corner of the pool where the guard can't see you.

You relax a bit in the warm mineral water and prepare to jump in time. You're looking for King Arthur, to see if the motto started with him, but you'll have to jump ahead in time to find him.

Ahead 150 years to A.D. 490.
Turn to page 65.

Ahead 250 years to A.D. 590.
Turn to page 75.

You're standing outside the town of Hennebonne, on the seacoast of Brittany, in northern France. The town is built like a castle, with high walls all around it.

Walking toward the town, you hear a whizzing sound. An arrow hits the ground in front of you! A guard on top of the walls just shot it, as a warning.

"Where did you come from?" he shouts. "What do you want?"

"I'm . . . from England," you shout.

"England!" He turns to shout to another guard. "A messenger from our English allies has arrived. Open the gates!"

The big iron gate is pulled up a crack, and you squeeze under it. They slam the gate behind you, and draw a bolt across it the size of a tree trunk.

"This way," the guard says. "Countess Jannedik wants to see you. Hurry! The French army is about to attack us again."

He must be taking you to see the Countess of Brittany, you decide. She's the person Sir Walter de Manny was coming to help. You wonder if he's arrived yet.

Men and women run everywhere through the streets and across the walls of the town. You see a woman in full battle-armor riding a big warhorse, directing the preparations for battle.

"Women of Brittany!" she shouts. "We must all prepare for battle!"

The guard pulls you up next to her horse. "Here is a messenger from England, my lady," he says.

"Well," she says to you, "what news from our English allies? Is King Edward sending help?"

"I'm not really a messenger," you say, "but I know that Sir Walter de Manny is on his way to help you."

Countess Jannedik jumps down from her horse. She grabs your hands. "Sir Walter!" she smiles. "The Lord be praised. Come."

You follow her up a steep flight of stone steps. She takes you to the highest turret of the castle.

Countess Jannedik peers out. "We've been holding off the attackers for weeks, but sooner or later their catapults will knock down our walls. Look—here they come again!"

You see an army approaching from the east.

"We need all the help we can get," Countess Jannedik says to you. "Please stay and help us defend ourselves."

She turns to command her soldiers. "Archers! Shoot at the ones with the catapults!" She goes off to direct the battle.

The army stops and lines up for battle. You hear a trumpet blow. Then the army runs forward, screaming a terrible war cry. Foot soldiers run up to the walls, carrying long wooden ladders.

The soldiers scream as the women on the walls pour boiling tar down on top of them. They fall off their ladders and lie groaning on the ground.

Arrows come whistling through the air. A woman screams, hit by an arrow. She tumbles over the edge. This sort of warfare can be pretty gruesome!

Soldiers pick up one of the big rocks. They place the rock on the back of a long bar on the giant catapult. They crank the long bar down with ropes.

A knight slices the rope in two. The bar snaps back, sending the rock flying toward the walls.

It's flying straight at you! You jump down a flight of stairs. The rock whistles past and smashes through a window of the building behind you.

The defenders of Hennebonne have a tough job ahead of them. Should you stay and help the Countess of Brittany? You'd find more knights if you left, jumping ahead to the battle of Crecy.

Stay and help the countess.
Turn to page 93.

Jump ahead to Crecy, 1346.
Turn to page 87.

ou're walking across a field near Crecy, France, toward an approaching army.

"You, peasant!" shouts a knight on horseback.

"Everyone must help defend France," he tells you. "You're drafted. Help those archers carry their arrows."

Now you're part of the *French* army! Blue banners with gold lilies on them flutter overhead—the symbol of the French kings. But how will you get to talk to the English king, Edward, if you're part of the enemy army? Only Edward knows what the motto on the garter means.

Well, for now you have no choice but to stick it out. You carry a load of arrows for the crossbowmen. They're paid professional fighters, using a heavy, elaborate sort of mechanical bow which they have to wind up.

"This is madness," one of the archers grumbles. "We march for eighteen miles, our bowstrings get wet in the rain, the whole army is completely disorganized, and already it is

the middle of the afternoon! Do they want us to shoot arrows in the dark? Why don't we stop, and fight tomorrow?"

"It's these foolish French knights," says another. "They think the English will be easy to beat. They cannot wait for the glory."

You can see that they're right. The French army *is* disorganized. It's all spread out in a line stretching for miles, while the English army is concentrated and waiting at the top of the hill.

The French knights behind you are confident, though. "Look at those English," one of them says scornfully, "standing there on the hill. Where are their horses? What kind of knight would choose to fight on *foot*?"

"You, archers!" shouts a knight from atop his horse. "You go first. Turn left when you get to the bottom. Then we knights will charge up the hill, and show these English cowards how to fight!"

The archers get their crossbows ready. "We're in range!" shouts their leader. The crossbowmen fire off a round of arrows. Then they spring back the handles of their machines, press on levers with their feet to draw the bows, and get new arrows ready.

Suddenly, the air is filled with arrows coming the other way! Arrows zip into the ground all around you.

"AARGH!" A crossbowman next to you drops his bow and screams as an arrow goes through his neck. You grab his shield and hide behind it.

"The English arrows, they fall like snow!" another archer shouts. "They do not stop!"

The English longbow must be five times faster than the crossbow. The shield you're crouching behind is beginning to look like a pincushion!

"This is too much," shouts the archer leader. But there's no place to run! Behind you is a line of knights on horseback.

"Cowards!" they yell at the archers. "Run away, will you? Run the varlets down!"

This is horrible! The knights trample down the frightened archers, part of their own army. They even swing their swords, killing their own men so they can charge up the hill at the English!

"Out of the way," a knight screams at you. "Let the real fighters through!" He raises his sword. You duck.

The sword never swings. You look up. An English arrow has gone right though the French knight's helmet. He tumbles off his horse.

Time to get *out* of here! Jump in time. Where? As far away as possible! Is there someone besides Edward who might know about the motto? Forget about finding King Edward—you'll look for King Arthur instead!

 Jump back 1000 years. Turn to page 80.

You decide to help Countess Jannedik defend the town. One of the rules of chivalry calls for knights to help women in distress. Countess Jannedik isn't a helpless damsel—she's a fierce warrior herself! But if you want to become a knight, you must act brave. Later, perhaps, you can jump ahead two years to the battle of Crecy.

The attacking army tires of trying to climb the walls. They pull their catapult out of range of the archers.

"Good work, my Bretons!" shouts Countess Jannedik from the walls. "Once more we have held them off. But they will return." She turns to you. "When will help from England arrive?"

"My lady!" a soldier shouts. "Look to the sea!"

Everyone runs to the top of the walls. You see a white sail against the blue sky, then another. Sir Walter de Manny has arrived!

"Prepare a feast," the countess commands, to celebrate the arrival of our valiant allies!"

 Welcome Sir Walter. Turn to page 98.

Y ou walk up the hill at Crecy. The banners at the top of the hill have three leopards on them. They must be the leopards of the kings of England. King Edward founded the Order of the Garter, so this is the right army for you to join.

When you get to the top of the hill, however, the English army is gone. All you see is a long line of helmets sitting on the ground. That's strange. Why did the knights leave their helmets here, and where have they gone? You look around.

You see the knights behind a windmill, with the army's supply wagons. The knights have gone off to eat while they wait for the French to arrive, leaving their helmets to mark their places in the battle order. This army is certainly well organized!

You walk along the row of helmets. Soon the helmets are replaced by rows of bows and arrows. This must be where the archers will fight.

A few steps ahead, two men in green clothes drag along what looks like a primitive cannon!

"Here, lend us a hand, will you," one of them calls to you. He looks familiar . . . yes! It's Tom, the yeoman farmer you met in Winchester in 1357. He told you he was an *archer* for

the king at Crecy. What is he doing with a cannon?

"Sure, Tom," you say as you push.

He squints at you. "How are you knowing my name, now?" He doesn't recognize *you*, of course. It will be eleven years before he meets you in Winchester!

"Why, because everybody knows you," you say. "You're Tom, with the cannon."

He smiles. "So already we cannoneers are well known, eh? Wait until the battle! King Edward himself will come a-thanking us, I don't doubt, for using this new contraption."

That's a thought. If you stay with Tom and his friends, you might be rewarded by King Edward when the new cannon surprises the French and wins the battle. That would give you a chance to ask the king about the Order of the Garter.

A trumpet sounds. "It's the signal," shouts Tom. "The French are coming up through the woods!" The knights and archers come running to their places.

Should you stay with Tom or go to where the knights are lining up to fight?

 Help Tom. Turn to page 113.

 Find the knights. Turn to page 107.

ou're lying on the back of a wooden cart. You can hear the trumpets and screams of the battle of Crecy in the distance. The cannon is gone, but your friend Tom is right next to you.

"I should be getting back to my bow now." Tom pats you on the shoulder. "Rest quiet. The doctor will be along soon. He'll empty out some of your bad blood, so you'll soon be ready to fight again."

You have to get out of here. The battle of Crecy may still be the right place to find Edward and become a knight, but it was a mistake to join the cannoneers instead of looking for the knights. You're in France . . . didn't Lady Joan's friend Sir Walter de Manny come to France to help the Countess of Brittany a couple of years ago?

Jump back two years to find Sir Walter de Manny. Turn to page 82.

You're sitting at a banquet table with Sir Walter and Countess Jannedik. Sir Walter wears a red eyepatch over his left eye.

"My good Sir Walter," says the countess, "have you hurt your eye?"

Sir Walter kisses her hand. "No, my lady. I have sworn never to take off this eyepatch until I have done a brave deed."

Countess Jannedik smiles. "You'll get your chance soon enough. But first, let the pipers play!"

Before the music can start, a huge rock comes smashing through the roof. It crashes to the floor, showering the room with dust. Countess Jannedik jumps to her feet. "The French are sending us gifts again," she says angrily, "with their giant catapult!"

"I'm afraid, madame, that this lovely dinner must wait. We will act at once!" He turns to his men. "We need fifty volunteers. Who will come with me?"

"I shall ride beside you," cries Countess Jannedik.

"We will, too!" shout Sir Walter's knights.

Countess Jannedik takes you aside.

"We will sneak out the back way," she says, "and attack the catapult from the rear. I want you to wait at the front gate. Open the gate for us when I signal you with my sword. Hurry!"

You run to the front gate. You climb to the top of the tower to watch for the countess's signal.

WHAM!

The gate shakes beneath you as a huge rock smashes into it. The attackers aim straight for the gate, hoping to smash it down so they can pour their army into the town.

Another crashing blow hits the gate. The iron creaks and bends, but so far it holds firm.

"Look there!" a guard shouts. Off in the distance you can see Sir Walter, the countess, and the fifty volunteers. They gallop along in their battle armor. There are so few of them! What can they hope to do?

Sir Walter tears off his eyepatch and spurs his horse. He shouts a fearsome war cry and rides straight at the army! The French knights are so surprised by this crazy attack, they turn and run away.

Countess Jannedik and the fifty knights rush after him, and in a few minutes they destroy the catapult.

"Hurrah!" shout the guards and archers.

The French knights soon come to their senses, though. When they realize how few

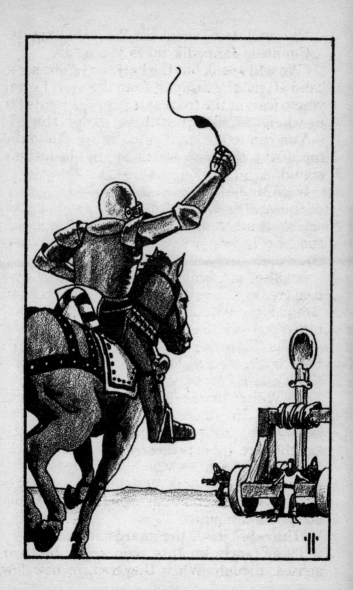

knights the countess has with her, they turn around.

Countess Jannedik waves her sword at you. It's the signal!

"Open the gates!" you shout to the guards. A horse pulls the rope that draws the gate up.

Sir Walter and Countess Jannedik ride toward you as fast as they can, with a thousand French knights chasing after them. The gate creaks open under you. The raiding party rushes into the town, welcomed by cheers. Now that the catapult has been destroyed, the attack will be easier to defeat.

Uh-oh. The rope holding the gate open is stuck! The gate is wide open for the attacking knights!

"Here!" Sir Walter shouts to you. "Use my sword. You're close enough to cut the rope in time!" Sir Walter's sword comes spinning up to you. You have to be careful you don't catch it by the sharp blade!

You catch it by the handle and crawl out across a narrow stone ledge. You duck as an arrow whisks past your ear. The rope is still far away! You have to stretch out and swing with the sword . . .

The rope slices in two. The iron gate falls with a crash, just as the galloping knights are about to ride through.

You reached out too far with the sword, though, and lost your balance. You're falling, right toward the knights below!

It's life or death for you now. Jump in time, quick!

Travel ahead two years to the battle of Crecy. Turn to page 74.

You run from the battle toward the part of the army held in reserve. You wonder if you made the right choice. You forgot to deliver the king's message. Not only that, but if part of your mission is to become a knight, why are you running away from danger? Above all, a knight must be brave!

An armored fist pinches your shoulder.

"What goes on up there?" growls the knight who holds you.

"A few French knights have gotten through, but the prince is fighting them," you say.

"Did you see a French knight with a blue cross on his shield?"

"No," you say. You try to pull away from this smelly knight, but he holds you tight.

"Have you heard mention of a knight named Sir Guy?" he growls. His eyes are fierce beneath his hairy face. "Two years ago, I swore a sacred oath. I swore I would never take a bath, nor cut my hair, until I beat that knight!"

You look closer at him. It's Sir Cuthbert, the knight you met at Windsor! He doesn't seem to recognize you. It's hard to recognize him, too—

he certainly *smells* like it's been two years since he took a bath!

"Sorry," you say. He lets you go. Time to make yourself scarce, you think. If Sir Cuthbert is here, that nasty squire of his must be, too! Should you jump in time? But where? You're in France, where Sir Walter de Manny was supposed to come to aid the Countess of Brittany. Perhaps you could go help him, to prove you're fit to be a knight.

"Aha!" You hear somebody calling you.

Oh no, it's Squire Randall! This time it's not a quarterstaff he is pointing at you but a sharp steel sword!

"Who are you, really?" he sneers. "You appear for a few days, then disapppear for years, without a trace! Where do you really come from?"

"I'm from . . . Navarre," you say.

"Oh, really?" he says with a smirk. He calls to another squire. "Carlos! You're from Navarre, right? Come here a moment."

A squire with dark curly hair comes up.

"This creature claims to be from Navarre, too," says Randall. "Is he?"

Carlos smiles. "A countryman! What a pleasure! How are things back in Pamplona?"

"Uh, fine," you say.

"How is King Theobald?"

"Well . . . as well as could be expected."

Carlos's smile turns into a scowl. "This is a faker, Randall. King Theobald has been dead for years!"

"Oho! So you're not from Navarre, eh?" Randall brings his sword up to rest against your throat. "Is it possible that you're a French spy? Yes! I think so. And in the middle of a war, a spy who's caught can expect no mercy!"

He twists his sword up toward your throat, but you're not about to let him cut your head off! You turn and run.

"Stop the spy!" You race off into the night, as fast as you can run. Randall has more armor on, so he's slower. You duck behind a wagon where no one can see you, and jump in time.

 Jump back two years to Brittany. Turn to page 82.

You say goodbye to Tom and walk behind the archers to the center of the hill, where the English knights wait for the French to attack. King Edward has split his army into three parts, you can see—two at the crest of the hill and one in reserve, in front of an old windmill. The knights line up in battle formation, presenting a row of shields to the enemy. Their squires wait for them behind the lines.

Someone grabs hold of your arm.

"You!" cries a squire wearing a breastplate and metal helmet. "What are you doing here?" He takes his helmet off.

It's your friend, Nigel! He looks older and more confident than he did in the days when he taught you how to be a squire. He should—for him, that was two years ago!

"I came to help," you say.

"Well, you're just in time. Here," he says excitedly, "I have an extra suit of armor you could wear. You'll need it. The battle is about to begin!"

He stops and looks at you strangely. You try

to stand a little taller, as if you were two years older, too.

"By the way," he says, "where have you been these last two years? We thought you'd gotten lost in the woods! Did you have to go back to Navarre suddenly?"

"Something like that," you say.

"You shouldn't just disappear like that without telling anyone," he says, punching you playfully on the shoulder. "But here we are, anyway. Put your helmet on. Here come the arrows!"

You put the helmet on as fast as you can and strap yourself into the breastplate. Putting on your armor helps you feel a little of what it's like to be a knight.

The English longbowmen fire back at the French archers. They send so many arrows flying that the enemy archers turn and run. A wave of French knights charges up the hill, but before they even get halfway up, the arrows cut them down.

"I cannot understand the French battle plan," Nigel says. "Why attack so late in the day? And why not organize themselves to attack all at once? They send a few knights at a time, to get slaughtered one by one!"

"This is horrible. What is all this fighting for, anyway?" you ask.

Nigel points to the flags fluttering above you.

"There's your answer," he says. "Both the

lilies of France and the leopards of England on King Edward's banners. He believes he should be king of *both* England and France."

"But that's silly," you say, "England and France are two different countries!"

Nigel stares at you. "Don't say such things!" he whispers. "Evil comes to those who think evil of the king's plans."

Nigel just said what sounded like the motto of the Order of the Garter! But before you can get him to explain it, you hear a whoosh and a crackling sound behind you. The windmill is in flames!

"Our own men set the fire," says Nigel. "It's getting so dark we can't see to fight without a giant torch."

You hear loud shouts from the English knights a few feet away. Some of the attackers are getting through! The lead attacker, a French knight on horseback, plunges into the ranks just ahead of you. The attacker swings a long, spiked club, bashing the heads of knights beneath him. He shouts a strange war cry: "Montjoie Saint Denis!"

A young knight with a leopard-covered tunic over his black armor slashes at the French knight with a sword.

"It's Prince Edward!" Nigel shouts.

More French knights make it though the arrows. The prince is in the center of a furious swordfight.

"Curse the day I was born," mutters Nigel.

"Here I stand, doing nothing! Will I ever have a chance to prove I can be a knight?"

"You, squires!" shouts one of the prince's knights. "One of you run to the king. Tell him we need reinforcements!"

You and Nigel look at each other.

"I'll go," you say. "They may soon need you here."

"Thank you, my friend!" Nigel says.

You run off toward the burning windmill.

The flames from the burning windmill rise fifty feet in the air.

This may be your chance to ask Edward about the motto!

The king stands in front of the burning mill, surveying the bloody battle on the hill below him.

"A message," you say breathlessly. "The prince needs reinforcements!"

Edward III stares down at you, a grim smile on his lips. "Is my son dead?" he asks quietly.

"No, sire."

"Has his banner fallen? Or does he still fight on?"

"He still fights," you say, "but he is well matched."

The king clasps you by the shoulders. "Tell those who sent you here not to send you again," he says, "as long as my son is alive. Tell them that my son must have the chance to win his spurs! Go!"

You didn't get a chance to ask the king

about the motto of the Order of the Garter. Maybe Nigel had the answer—could the motto have to do with the king's ambition to be king of two countries at once?

The prince and his friends are still battling the French knights when you return, but something is missing from the scene. Then you see what it is—the prince's banner has fallen! The official flag carrier is busy dueling with a French knight and has let the banner fall to the ground.

The banner is very important to the knights. Should you rush into the middle of the battle and pick the banner up? Or should you run back to the reserves, where the king is, and try to figure out a way to speak with him again?

Pick up the prince's banner. Turn to page 115.

Go back to the king's reserves. Turn to page 104.

You're standing with Tom by the cannon among a group of English archers. Trumpets sound the call to battle. The archers take their bowstrings out of their helmets, where they keep them dry. They have to pull with all their strength to bend their mighty bows so the strings will fit on them.

"I hope this works," Tom says as you help him roll a round stone into the fat mouth of the cannon. "It's never been tried in battle before. I'd be much happier with a bow in my hands, but when you're in an army you do what you are told!" So Tom really was an archer!

Down below, you see the French army approaching. The army is all spread out and disorganized, but it is far larger than the English forces with you on the hill.

"Look there," says Tom with surprise. "Archers! I thought the French knights didn't believe in archery."

"Those are Italian crossbowmen," an archer says. "They were hired by the French!"

"Ready," the English archers' commander shouts.

The archers draw back their bows and wait.

"Hyaaagh!" comes a shout from the French army below. Thick, short arrows from the crossbows zip over your head.

"Shoot at will!" shouts the commander. "Stand back," says Tom. He holds a burning torch in his hand and uses it to set off the cannon.

KABOOM! A huge cloud of smoke erupts from the cannon. The stone, however, just bloops about fifteen feet down the hill and sticks in the ground.

"Bah," says Tom. "We might as well *roll* the stones down the hill!"

It will be a long time, you guess, before battles are won using guns. This is not the way to get King Edward to help you!

"I'm going to try it once more," Tom says, "then I'll get my bow and join the archers, where I belong."

He puts the torch to the cannon, but nothing happens.

"Watch out," screams Tom. "It's going to explode!"

You jump for cover, but not fast enough. The last things you see before you lose consciousness are the flash of gunpowder and the ground rushing up to meet you.

 Turn to page 97.

ou watch the prince
and his knights battle the French knights by
the flickering yellow light of the burning mill.
The banner lies on the ground, trampled un-
derfoot. You pick up a shield and wait for an
opening.

There! The way to the banner is clear. You
rush in to pick it up. Just as you reach it,
someone else's hand grabs the pole. It's Nigel!
You smile at each other as you raise the banner high.

"Hurrah!" cry the fighting knights as they
see their banner fly again.

The clink and clank of crossing swords is all
around you. From the ground come the the
shrieks of the wounded and the groans of the
dying.

You hold your shield up as a knight runs at
you with his sword. Another knight comes at
him from the side and slices off his arm with a
battle-ax. The first knight's arm, still holding
the sword, falls at your feet.

You look at Nigel. His mouth is set in a
tight, brave smile, but his eyes show fear and
horror. So *this* is the glamorous "sport" the
knights are so very fond of? You prefer the

tournaments to this bloody, senseless killing. But knights were warriors, and war is always bloody and cruel.

You're not sure how much more of this you can take. Soon, though, the French knights who got through the lines are all killed or captured.

The prince and his friends stick their swords in the ground and lean on them to rest.

"Where is the messenger we sent to the king?" calls a tall, one-eyed knight.

"Here I am," you say. Leaving Nigel to hold the banner pole, you walk forward.

"The king told me to tell you," you say, "not to send for reinforcements unless his son was killed. He said the prince must earn his spurs."

The one-eyed knight turns to the prince. Blood from a gash on the prince's cheek drips down on his black chain mail.

"Earn his spurs?" says the knight. "I should say the young prince has earned them. He has earned them ten times over!"

"Hurrah for Prince Edward!" shout the knights.

The Black Prince pulls his sword from the ground and walks forward.

"It is not only I who have earned the spurs of knighthood," he says. "I saw two squires bravely enter the thick of battle to rescue my banner. Kneel, squire!" he commands you.

You kneel down in the blood-soaked grass in

front of him. The prince holds out his sword. The blade is so nicked and dented by the fighting that it looks like the blade of a saw. He taps the side of the sword on your right shoulder, then your left.

"Arise, knight," he says. "Be true to your lord, your honor, and your lady fair."

Then he calls Nigel forward and performs the same ceremony for him.

You've done it! You've been knighted, by the Black Prince himself! Nigel turns to you and smiles, fighting back tears of joy.

The battle goes on late into the night, but finally the French army is defeated. The exhausted English knights lie down to sleep, right in the field of battle.

You still have to find out what the motto of the Order of the Garter means, but now that you're a knight, it should be easier to complete your mission. None of the knights here wear garters on their arms yet. Does it have to do with the king's plans that brought about this battle?

You know that your friend Nigel, now *Sir* Nigel, will become a member of the order. The other members could be the knights sleeping all around you, though they may not know it yet.

 Jump ahead two years to Windsor. Turn to page 119.

You're back in Windsor, on April 23, 1348. You're standing in the shadows of a courtyard of the castle. A crowd of people watches a long carriage pulled by four black horses enter through the gate. A woman gets out of the carriage, dressed in a beautiful white gown. She goes through a door to a large hall. You can hear music playing inside.

You see a long-haired, frizzy-bearded knight sitting on a block of stone nearby. He looks very sad.

"What is happening?" you ask him.

"The guests are arriving for the king's ball," he says. "I, too, was invited, but they will not let me in."

"Why not?"

"Who would want to dance," he says sadly, "with a poor knight whose last bath was taken four long years ago?"

You look at him. It's Sir Cuthbert! He's the knight who swore never to cut his hair or take a bath until he beat Sir Guy. He's kept his oath, all right. No wonder they won't let him in. He smells terrible!

A group of knights dressed in silk and satin arrive on horseback and dismount. You try to follow them in, but a guard blocks your path.

"Only knights and ladies invited by the king are allowed in," he tells you. "Stand aside!"

He pushes you back with a long spear, sending you sprawling over the cobblestones. People laugh. You pick yourself up and turn to go. You don't care about their stupid ball anyway!

"In the name of St. George!" You hear a familiar voice. It's your friend Nigel! *Sir* Nigel, now. He stares at you with astonishment.

"We thought you were killed," he says, "on the battlefield at Crecy!" He turns to the guard and scowls. "This is a hero of Crecy," he says sternly. "If anyone should be admitted to the king's ball, it should be this noble knight!"

You follow him in to a large hall lined with tapestries and lit with torches. Knights and ladies dance back and forth in long lines. The prince and the king dance with their ladies.

"I don't know how you've come back to us," Nigel says, "but welcome, welcome! The king has invited all the heroes of Crecy to the tournament tomorrow. But tonight we dance!"

A young woman in a long gown comes up to Nigel. You recognize her—it's Lady Joan of Kent, the one you last saw hunting with falcons. Nigel turns and shrugs to you. He and Joan join the line of dancers.

You sit down at a table near a giant fireplace, across from a knight wearing long, pointed shoes.

"That was Lady Joan, was it not?" he says to you. "Have you heard the latest rumor? She and Prince Edward are in love!"

So that's her secret. Joan always said she was in love with a very noble knight—it turns out it's the prince himself!

"Why aren't you dancing?" you ask the knight.

He rolls his eyes. "Oh, I don't really feel like it. I'm here as a prisoner, after all. I'm a French knight, captured at the battle of Crecy. Noble prisoners are treated very well—I sit here fighting in tournaments, going to balls, and playing chess. But imagine. It's been two years since I've seen my home in France."

The music stops and the dancers drift apart. Lady Joan and Nigel stand talking with the king in the middle of the hall. There's something round sitting there on the floor, made of blue cloth. The king bends down to pick it up.

All across the hall, people watch the king and laugh, quietly. What's so funny? You see Lady Joan blushing. It must be a garter he's holding, which was holding up Lady Joan's stocking, but fell off.

"It's the king himself who picks up Lady Joan's garter," some ladies near you whisper, "but it's really the prince she loves!" The crowd falls silent when they see the king is about to speak.

"It has been four years," he says loudly, "since I promised to start a new Round Table of knights, like that of King Arthur. Tomorrow I will choose thirty of my noblest knights to honor above all others." He waves the garter above his head, "This will be our symbol. *Honi soit qui mal y pense! May* evil come to those who think evil of it!"

He signals the musicians, and the dancing starts again.

He's said the famous motto! At last you know where the words come from! The king first uses them to silence whispers about a secret romance, and then gets the idea to use the garter as the symbol of his knights.

"You look disappointed about something," the French knight says to you. "What's the matter?"

"How would you feel," you say, "if you went through all sorts of dangers to find something. Then when you found what you were looking for, it wasn't what you thought it was at all?"

He smiles. "That's the way it is with most knightly quests. The knights of the Round Table spent their lives looking for the Holy Grail, but most of them never found it. It doesn't matter so much what you're searching for as much as how you look for it, what you find along the way, and how much you can help the other people searching."

"Here," he says, bringing out a leather bag full of chess pieces. "Let's have a game of chess, to take your mind off your troubles."

"Thanks, Sir . . . uh . . ."

"Sir Guy is my name."

Sir Guy! He's the knight Sir Cuthbert swore he would beat some day. That gives you an idea.

"I don't feel like playing much," you tell him, "but I have a friend outside who would

love to play with you. Come on!"

You take Sir Guy outside, where Sir Cuthbert sits with his head on his hands. Sir Cuthbert is startled to be face to face with his old enemy, but smiles when you whisper your idea in his ear.

The two knights set the pieces up and play. Sir Guy, you can tell, is eager to get the game over with so he can get away from his awful-smelling opponent. In a short time, the game is over. Sir Cuthbert has won.

"Praise God!" he cries, knocking over the table as he jumps to his feet. "I've won! Now I may take a bath again!" Sir Guy looks at him as if he were crazy. Sir Cuthbert whoops with delight and hugs you with gratitude.

You slip out of his arms, and into the shadows of the castle while he dances up and down with glee.

It's too bad, you think as you prepare to jump back to your own time, that the knights didn't learn to solve their disputes with chess instead of war. They still haven't learned that lesson well enough back where you're going, but all the same you're glad to be going back home.

Congratulations! You have reached the end of your quest.

MISSION COMPLETED.

DATA FILE

Page 8: This type of harness is not meant for a horse.

Page 12: You can hide in either, but only in one can they go-seek.

Page 14: How well should a knight know how to shoot arrows?

Page 19: What arrived in England in 1348?

Page 29: To every thing there is a season, including disease.

Page 41: Have you seen this boy before?

Page 44: Will you want to meet the visitor that arrived from overseas in 1348?

Page 56: You can trust what your friend Nigel tells you.

Page 58: How does one become a knight?

Page 64: Is there something fishy about trial by water?

Page 73: How much could the people of King Edward's time know about King Arthur?

Page 74: Golden leopards appear in the signs of certain kings.

Page 79: Flattery may get you somewhere when a king asks for a song about a king.

Page 80: The year 90 A.D. is part of which century?

Page 86: A knight should try to live up to the code of chivalry.

Page 96: When will they really get a bang out of cannons?

Page 112: A knight must live by the code of chivalry.

About the Contributors

JIM GASPERINI reviews interactive computer fiction for *Electronic Fun,* and published the history of a medieval french artisan's guild in *Museum.* He has been a videotape editor, a busker, a traveling book salesman, a literary agent and made his operatic debut in the 1983 Metropolitan Opera's production of *Don Carlo* as Arquebusier (spear-carrier). He resides in New York.

RICHARD HESCOX is an illustrator whose paperback book covers and illustrations have had world-wide distribution. His work has covered such diverse fields as magazine illustration, advertising, record album covers and production designs for films including *The Howling* and *A Trip To Tomorrow.* He has painted movie posters for *Swamp Thing, E.T., The Dark Crystal,* and other features. Some of his fantasy work has been published in a portfolio entitled *A Fatal Beauty.* He resides in Hollywood, California.

CHOOSE YOUR OWN ADVENTURE ®

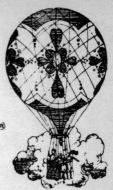

"You'll want all the books in the exciting Choose Your Own Adventure series. Each book takes you through dozens of fantasy adventures—under the sea, in a space colony, into the past—in which *you* are the main character. What happens next in the story depends on the choices *you* make, and *only you* can decide how the story ends!"